Words

The Letterlanders love to make their sounds in words.

b... u... sss...

hhh... a... t...

d... o... g...

Remind your child that they can always use the special Letterland trick to remember any sound they have forgotten. Just start to say a Letterlander's name, then stop! Dippy Duck's sound is a quick 'd...' sound (with mouth almost shut), not 'dee' or 'duh'!

Starting words

Say the first sound in each Letterlander's name.

Annie Apple

Bouncy Ben

Clever Cat

Whose sound starts each word? Write the letter. Read the word.

bus

_nt

_at

_ed

_up

_pple

Listen

After saying the sounds at the top together, look at the pictures underneath. Can your child tell you the first sound he or she hears in the word 'bus'? Which Letterlander makes that sound?

Say the first sound in each Letterlander's name.

 d  e  f  g

Dippy Duck   **Eddy Elephant**   **Firefighter Fred**   **Golden Girl**

Whose sound starts each word? Write the letter. Read the word.

_og

_gg

_ox

_uck

_reen

_rog

When you have helped your child to finish the page, stop and let him or her have fun
pretending to be a **f**irefighter **f**ighting **f**ires with **f**oam as you make Firefighter Fred's '**fff**…' sound.

Starting words

Say the first sound in each Letterlander's name.

Harry Hat Man   Impy Ink   Jumping Jim   Kicking King

Whose sound starts each word? Write the letter. Read the word.

_am   _at   _ug

_and   _ing   _nsect

Letter sounds

Ask your child if they remember the Letterland trick for discovering any letter sound. (See page 3).
For '**hhh**...', you can also try creating mist on a mirror. For '**j**...', keep your mouth almost shut, and for
'**k**...', just whisper the sound to avoid adding 'uh'.

Say the first sound in each Letterlander's name.

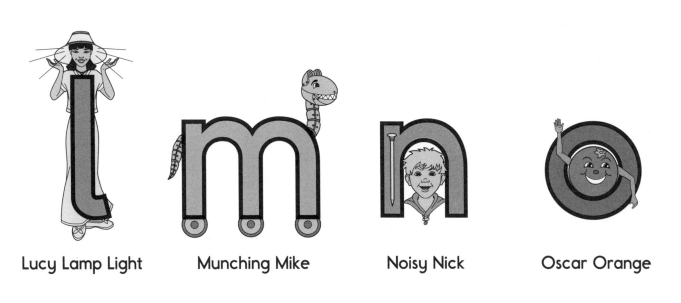

Lucy Lamp Light   Munching Mike   Noisy Nick   Oscar Orange

Whose sound starts each word? Write the letter. Read the word.

_ut   _og   _ug

_n   _at   _et

Blends

After writing in the missing letter, encourage your child to run a finger under each letter and slowly say the sounds, blending them together to make the word. Later, encourage your child to practise sounding out some of these words again.

5

Starting words

Say the first sound in each Letterlander's name.

Peter Puppy   Quarrelsome Queen   Red Robot   Sammy Snake

Whose sound starts each word? Write the letter. Read the word.

_ed   _ix   _an

_in   _un   _uilt

Letter sounds

Pretend to be Quarrelsome Queen as you shake your index finger and say her sound.
(It should sound as though you are just about to say, 'Quiet!')
Have fun making Sammy Snake's sound together. He likes to hiss in words: 'sss...'.

Say the first sound in each Letterlander's name.

Talking Tess   **Uppy Umbrella**   **Vicky Violet**   **Walter Walrus**

Whose sound starts each word? Write the letter. Read the word.

   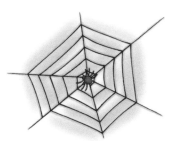

_en   _an   _eb

_op   _et   _p

Stories

Every Letterlander loves things that start with his or her own sound. Try making up brief stories together about the Letterlanders and the things on these pages that start with their sounds.

7

Starting words

Say the last sound in Max's name. Say the first sound in the others.

Fix-it Max

Yellow Yo-yo Man

Zig Zag Zebra

Whose sound is missing? Write the letter. Read the word.

_ip

_ak

bo_

fo_

_ebra

_ellow

Read a-z!

Try going back and pointing to the Letterland characters at the top of pages 4-10, saying their names aloud together. Can your child hear the characters' sound twice in each of their names? Did he or she spot Max's sound at the end of his name?

Ending words

Say Munching Mike's sound.

Say Noisy Nick's sound.

Name the picture below. Whose sound can you hear at the end of the word? Circle the word that matches the picture.

jam   jan

tem   ten

pem   pen

fam   fan

Read

After your child has named each picture, help him or her to read the two words under the picture. Are they both real words? You may like to explain here that only real words have meaning. Non-words don't mean anything.

9

Ending words

Say Dippy Duck's sound.

Say Golden Girl's sound.

Name the picture below. Whose sound can you hear at the **end** of the word? Circle the word that matches the picture.

jug   jud

beg   bed

dog   dod

reg   red

Nonsense

Reading nonsense words is good practice! Try saying each word together.
Is it a real word? Does it match the picture? If so, circle it.

Say Peter Puppy's sound.

Say Talking Tess's sound.

Name the picture below. Whose sound can you hear at the end of the word? Circle the word that matches the picture.

cat   cap   hap   hat

pot   pop   hop   hot

Rhyme Can your child find a word that rhymes with **cat** (**hat**)? Can you find a word that rhymes with **pop**? Later on, try *My First Rhyming Activity Book* and have fun emphasising the rhyming words together.

11

In the middle

Say Annie Apple's sound.

Say Eddy Elephant's sound.

Name each picture below. Whose sound can you hear in the middle of each word? Write in the missing letter.

m a n

m _ n

h _ t

b _ d

Read!

After your child has completed the page, try covering each picture and encourage him or her to try reading the word.

Say Impy Ink's sound.

Say Eddy Elephant's sound.

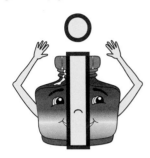

Name each picture below. Whose sound can you hear in the middle of each word? Write in the missing letter.

w_n

10

t_n

p_g

p_g

Read!

Encourage your child to try this game when you have finished this page (and other pages). Take turns closing your eyes and putting your finger somewhere on the lower part of the page. Then read the word closest to where your finger landed.

13

In the middle

Say Oscar Orange's sound.

Say Uppy Umbrella's sound.

Name each picture below. Whose sound can you hear in the middle of each word? Circle the matching word.

hot   hut

hut   hot

dog   dug

nut   not

Letter sounds

Uppy **U**mbrella makes the sound you hear in '**U**p, **u**p and away!' Try opening your mouth wide for Oscar's sound so your child can see the difference.

Say Annie Apple's sound.

Say Uppy Umbrella's sound.

Name each picture below. Whose sound can you hear in the middle of each word? Circle the matching word.

bug   bag

bug   bag

hut   hat

sun   san

Read! Ask your child to read just the words that have Annie Apple's sound in the middle. Then read only the words with Uppy Umbrella's sound in the middle.

15